My Life in Home Health Nursing
(A Forty-Plus Year Journey)

Marjorie Reid

DEDICATION

To all nurses, home health aides who are rewarded by this career

Also, for my family who have been a part of this journey

CONTENTS

The stories written here come from events that happened during my forty plus career in home health nursing and administration. The situations that prompted my writings are real, but I used creative ideas to elaborate on some of the moments.
Names have been changed when necessary.

Finding Treasure in the Attic

Parking my car in front of the Visiting Nurse Association's garage on a cool September morning, I walk to the door. Saturday morning, all is quiet on the street, though evidence of last night's revelry from the bar across the street lay in the gutter. I feel uneasy with my recent position as Nursing Director. Leading the nursing team was a new challenge. The ink on my graduate degree was fresh and I was replacing a well-loved, retiring lady who held this role for twenty-five years. The words Pete, the agency's black janitor, echo in my mind. He told me one evening, when everyone had left for the day: "They call you Nurse Ratched". I thought of the stern fictional character from "One Flew Over the Cuckoo Nest". His comments remind me that I need to listen to the nurses and, as he advised, "smile more".

The nonprofit VNA owned the 1940s brick two-story building as central offices for nurses and aides who provide home care and public health services to the Davenport, Iowa and surrounding rural areas. My office was on the corner of the first floor, while staff nurses and supervisors occupied the rest of that floor. Home health aide services and financial/billing employees occupied the basement. The spacious attic, or second floor, was used for storage. Patients who no longer needed crutches, or bedpans, or other aids gave them to well-meaning nurses. Physicians gave medication samples to the agency, where they were placed in boxes for attic storage.

Recent changes in the Medicare regulations opened access for patients that need home care services. No longer was a three-day hospital stay required to receive Medicare payment for skilled care services in the comfort of home. In the early 1980's, an era of medical advances to extend life, more patients were treated in their homes. In response to these changes, the VNA Board determined it was time to expand office facilities to meet the growing need for services. This meant moving financial/billing staff to the attic. When asked if I would clear out the attic storage, I jumped at the chance, believing this could lead to finding clues to success in this business.

Musty odors envelop me when I opened the attic door. Shelves of discarded devices used to treat patients fill one side of the spacious room. File cabinets lined up in rows, like metal soldiers, stand in the middle of the room. Large cardboard boxes filled with medication bottles and assorted wound care supplies are stacked at to the right of the stair door. My eyes sweep the dimly lit room. I wonder whether this is more than I can manage. The street is quiet on the Saturday morning, my family asleep at home. Taking a deep breath, I throw my coat over the stair rail and step into the room.

Tackling file cabinets is my first task. Inside are hand-written and typed documents from decades past. I weed through the papers like a pirate seeking to find gold. Here was history a healing service to the sick, infirm and poor of this small town and rural community. As a lover of history, I read of the Florence Nightingale's work in Crimea and recalled the school ritual for students to carry a lamp during the class ceremony that marked entry to the nursing school. This silent trek through history of the VNA could release treasures that tell the tale of early home and community health.

To my dismay, most of the ancient written recordings in the file cabinets carry no lasting value to present day services. My eyes scan page after page, until coming across a hand-written document where the annual meeting of a 1933 VNA Board of Directors is recorded. The first entry on this paper document lists the names of women who brought "delicacies" to the meeting, followed by names of the seven lay board members. The following notes demonstrated a peek into the changing role of the nurse. During that year, one nurse made over 18,000 visits to sick and indigent residents of the city: providing health education, hands-on-care, and teaching methods to prevent the spread of disease. This extraordinary feat was accomplished during summer heat and winter storms – many of the visits on horseback. My imagination swirls as I read about this unnamed nurse's devotion to the poor, elderly and sick in our community. She had no concerns for regulations or reimbursement or lengthy documentation, as is necessary for today's nurses. Her only interest, it seems, was to help those in need. This treasure deserved to be saved. I placed it aside to be framed as a remembrance of her passion. (It now hangs on the entrance wall of the agency to remind staff and visitors of the value of home health to the community.)

On the left side of the room are wooden shelves filled with bedpans, some large, some small, some metal, many glass and ceramic. Twenty pairs of crutches and a dozen walkers lean up against the far wall. Before government regulations, nurses often accepted donations of used crutches to help those who could not afford new devices. Giving used crutches to a patient -today- would violate safety standards. With a sigh, I sorted through the crutches, and find only two pair solid enough to donate to a community charity. The remaining pairs were sent for disposal, a symbol of our "throw-away" culture. The bedpans and urinals were thrown, as well.

Two large metal cabinets on the far side of the room house x-ray images of lungs, likely taken during the 1940's, when annual films of tuberculosis patients was common practice. I thought of a time when public health vans arrived in every Iowa town to provide free x-rays for persons who had tested positive for tuberculosis. As a child, I tested positive to a skin test for tuberculin exposure. Mother escorted me to the large van for chest x-rays, despite my reluctance to enter the scary behemoth appearing bus. The stored x-ray images in the VNA attic are coated with a silver substance used during early radiology techniques. They were designated to be sold for the mineral deposits.

In the center of the sparsely lighted room is a wooden bookshelf with textbooks on topic as: human anatomy, microbiology and nutrition. One dusty blue book with yellowed pages catches my eye. The title is simply: Public Health Nursing by Mary S. Gardner, written in 1916. Here could be the treasure I hoped to find. My pulse quickens as I lifted down the volume and dust the cover. Within these pages there could be jewels of wisdom from yesterday's nurses that might transfer to today. My sorting through the attic remnants stops. Sitting on the floor, I open the front cover, read the chapter titles and know this was meant to be included with my personal collection of favorite books. Later, I took it home and continue to treasure it as insight into qualities of my chosen profession.

On the inside cover of the book, "Chapter 18", was written in pencil, as though directing me to open to that page. The title of the chapter is one that I had long pondered during my last year as a nursing student: "Shall I Become a Public Health Nurse?" Several sentences in the first paragraph of that chapter are underlined, communicating that home care nursing was not for everyone: "All nurses do not make good public health nurses". Qualities listed for success in this career are: "capable of working cooperatively; interested in teaching; and able to think in terms of community welfare and general public health". I paused as I read the teachings of history and ponder my decision to join the

Visiting Nurse Organization. My choice, if I was honest, was based

on a selfish wish to have a position where I could use my new

leadership skills and earn a level of prestige. With chagrin, I

continue to read.

Opening paragraphs of the chapter spoke of qualities that

are assets for home health nurses from early days to today. In

making a decision to enter this field of endeavor, the book

describes three considerations. First, "the work chosen must to

worth doing" (no argument there); second: "such work must not

destroy the nurse's health or happiness" (good advice), and third:

"she should receive suitable financial remuneration" (equal pay is

a current topic of dispute). To support the written statements of

necessary qualities for a public health nurse, the author provides

additional arguments. Her statements on the need to maintain

good health and happiness made me pause.

"It is hard work", she writes. My thoughts wander to my

decision to work long days, leaving for home when dusk was

arriving. Further, she writes, "For a nurse with physical weak points, such as a delicate throat or heart that makes walking or climbing steps undesirable, other work may be better". I remembered lugging a clumsy baby scale up narrow stairs to visit a mother and infant living on the second floor of a vacant building. My anxiety level rose when climbing the narrow stairs but was immediately diffused when viewing the mother's smile.

The teenage new mother, Sara, was alone with the responsibility of caring for her infant son. She had no crib and few baby clothes. The baby was wrapped in a blanket with "St. Luke's Hospital" printed on the edge. After weighing the baby and completing a basic examination, I provided tips for care. We located a dresser drawer, lined it with bed linens for padding and made a crib for baby. Placing a call to a community service, I arranged for diapers and clothes to be delivered. Time for teaching about breast feeding, safety and more. I left and promised to return the next morning.

Later in the chapter, the writer discusses the need to consider the nurses "happiness". I thought of Sharon, who grinned with joy after her visits to a twenty-year old man with advanced colon cancer. His frail body bedridden, the room reeked with an odor of body waste when entering his room. Sharon told me of teaching his mother ostomy care, while she chatted with the patient. When she began packing up her stethoscope and blood pressure equipment to leave his home, he said with a smile "next time bring pizza and a beer". This request to her came at the end of each weekly visit. Weeks later, she received a late evening phone-call from his mother, asking Sharon to make a last visit. She rushed to his bedside with tears in her eyes and held his hand. Before losing consciousness, he gazed at her face and said: "hope you brought the pizza and beer". For most hospice nurses who choses this work, happiness comes from knowing your care has eased a difficult process of life's journey.

A chapter of the treasured book entitled "The Director" had been flagged with small cardboard squares labeled with "Visiting Nurse Assoc. TAG DAY 1913, for the SICK POOR". Here was evidence of early 20th century fund drive for continued services to the needy of this small city. Despite changes in health insurance regulations, many people may not have an ability to pay for home health. The cardboard squares signal that my role may require leadership for the financial balance to meet needed services.

....

The collection of writings in this volume were written to record my home health experiences in a forty-year career, working in more than four states. My goal is not to reward my work, but to highlight what I learned from the patients and caregivers. I leave this account as a legacy for my children and the many home health nurses who continue to bring healing care and comfort to a community.

Consider the Stethoscope

Simple instrument dangles about the nurse's neck,

Believed to have power for unlocking mysteries of the body.

Ancient necklace, provides a tether to the patient,

Like a towrope to rescue stranded vessels on stormy seas.

Basic tool of the trade: as a painter's brush, a mathematician's pencil.

Revered medal of honor, it signals medical skill to the sick and infirm.

Using the stethoscope requires human touch and quiet listening,

Sending a silent message of acceptance and care.

Device to diagnose heart murmurs, congested lung sounds.

With a stethoscope and careful listening, perhaps a priest

Could find a pathway to your soul.

Lessons from Annie

Overgrown shrubs almost enveloped the gray shack; weeds draped over the broken sidewalk that curved to her front door. Hard to believe anyone lives inside this house, I thought. Parking my Volkswagen beside the curb, I pulled the daily assignment sheet to confirm the address. No mistake. Inside this run-down place I should find eighty-five-year old Annie Ireland, who had a new diagnosis of insulin-dependent diabetes. My home health assignment was to teach her about insulin.

This was my first solo patient assignment after college graduation. Growing up in a small, affluent Midwestern town, the only scenes of poverty I knew were those flashed on movie screens or described in books. I stepped out of my car, locked the door, and glanced around the empty street. I shivered, not from the cold, but from thinking about being alone. The shack resembled one of those desolate buildings where vagrants find shelter. Common sense told me to leave, but I didn't.

I walked through the weeds to the front door and knocked, as I pulled my coat close against the brisk autumn breeze. In the lot's corner, a rusted auto wheel and broken sink are buried in the dirt. There were no sounds from inside the house. For a minute, my shoulders relaxed with a sense of relief. I knocked again before walking away from the front door. Pinching my lips, I pulled my nursing bag close and prayed that this was a vacant house.

Then I heard a groan and soft shuffling steps. I felt like running, but knew that wouldn't be right. I was here as a nurse and should ignore the twinge creeping up my neck. The front door opened a few inches. A small woman with stringy, grey hair and a beak-like nose peered at me. She was as tall as a middle school girl, with a wrinkled, weathered face and black eyes. A gust of wind blew brown leaves off the elm tree and across the yard. No possible retreat now, I thought.

"Annie Ireland?" I asked. My nursing bag hung like a bag of bricks on my arm.

"What do you want?" she rasped. Her tone was abrasive. She raised one hand to shield her eyes from the outside light.

"Your doctor sent me to help you with your insulin. I'm a nurse." My 1960s nursing license new, and I felt like an imposter imitating a home health nurse. I thought about the nursing lab at school where we practiced injecting sterile water into oranges. I wondered whether anything I learned in the classroom would make any difference in the real world.

Annie nodded, made chewing motions with her mouth and looked at me with those piercing dark eyes. With a shrug, she opened the door. I walked inside on bare floor-boards that moved with each step. The small room was dark with a musty odor that reminded me of the smell in a used bookstore. My eyes slowly adjusted to the dim light from a single bulb hanging from the middle of the ceiling. Just inside the door, a dingy, pale pink sheet is tossed over an upholstered chair. Stacks of newspapers sat next on the floor. On one side of the room was a small refrigerator, no larger than one I had in my dorm room at college. Next to it was a round Formica top table, once yellow, now faded and worn. Its rusty metal legs curved to remains of a checkered linoleum floor.

I sized up the room and decided to set up a workspace on the Formica table. I slid off my coat and draped it over a wooden kitchen chair. Placing my nursing bag on the table, I pulled out my supplies. Annie moved closer. Her mousey-grey hair fell to her bony shoulders. She wore a patterned blue cotton dress, with an oversized navy cardigan that hung down to her knees. Beige knee-high stockings flopped down over her ankles. Grimy red slippers covered her feet.

On the opposite wall was a small metal frame bed with a bare mattress, two pillows, no pillowcases. I heard a low moan, turned , and saw an elderly man lying in the bed. He cleared his throat and swung his legs over the edge of the mattress to sit up.

"Oh, hello," I said. "Sorry, I didn't see you there. I'm Annie's nurse."

"No good comes from doctors or medicines," he said. "Waste of money, 'swat it is."

"Keep quiet, Joe. It's my social security, not yours." Annie wiped her mouth with the back of her hand. "Promised the doc, and this young thing is doing her best."

Joe muttered, "Never saw a nurse worth anything." He lowered his eyes and stood. He was unshaven and had a thick mane of hair, dressed in stained blue boxer shorts and a grey-white undershirt. Walking as though every step caused his knees to ache, he moved to a doorway at the end of the room where he stopped and reached for an empty jelly jar on a shelf. He opened the door and I saw the toilet inside the tiny bathroom. With the empty jelly jar, he scooped up water from the toilet bowl and drank. My throat tightened, and I blinked my eyes to ward off a sense of nausea that rose from my gut.

"Today, I'll show you how to draw up the insulin in a syringe. Soon, you will manage this," I said. I placed insulin syringes, alcohol swabs and my hand washing supplies on the table. "Very important that you have an injection every morning," I said. My voice sounded hollow. I was chattering to fill the empty void inside. My words helped me to focus on the reason for my visit, to teach Annie about her disease. How would an old lady, living in this place ever learn to manage her disease, I wondered? It seemed as though failure was inevitable.

Annie, with hands on her hips, smacked her lips. "Guess you need the medicine," she muttered, as she shuffled away. She moved to the refrigerator and retrieved a bottle of insulin. I tried to see whether there was anything else in that refrig, but couldn't without appearing obvious.

We went through routines with Annie on that first morning. Teaching her about keeping her diabetic supplies clean,

I washed my hands at her kitchen sink, drew up the

insulin into a syringe and injected it into her weather-worn body.

She remained silent, but vigilant during the entire process.

Moving as in rote, I placed the used needle into a red sharps

container that I pulled from my nursing bag and handed Annie the

insulin vial.

"Done for today," I announced. I grabbed my coat and

started toward the door before thinking to ask whether she had

questions. I paused and looked back at her. She sat at the table,

one hand rubbing her forehead.

"You need to eat breakfast," I said. "Something with

protein to keep your blood sugar stable. The insulin will act on

your body within the next thirty minutes, so food is important." I

thought about the lunch box in my car and considered offering

that as her breakfast, if necessary.

"Yes, miss," Annie replied and stood to usher me to the

front door. "Got bread and bologna in the icebox."

"Tomorrow, I'll be here in the morning," I said. As I followed the broken sidewalk away from the house, I wondered whether home health nursing was right for me. Had I made any progress with this one patient? Did Annie sense my disgust with her environment?

I kept my thoughts to myself. When the senior nurses asked about my diabetic patient, I said it was "fine, just fine." No need to talk about my gut reaction at the home of Annie and her male friend. How she spent her days and nights was not my worry. Helping her to learn to manage her insulin and meals was my only job.

Annie was my first patient visit for the next seven days. Each morning seemed a little easier for me. I didn't notice the peeling paint on the front door anymore than I did the dank room odor. Even Joe fell into the routine and raised his hand in greeting when I arrived. I saw him clear the table to make room for my supplies.

One morning, the robins chirped as I walked to the front door. Annie had been watching for me and held the door open. Her lips had a slight upturn and eyes seemed to shine. She reminded me of a schoolgirl who wants to show off for her teacher. I placed my nursing bag on her table and sat on a wooden chair, ignoring the cluttered room.

"Just sit and watch," she said. I was quiet as she walked to the sink to wash her hands, wiping them on her skirt. She continued to draw up insulin in a syringe and injected it into her left thigh. Her technique was not perfect, but better than I had expected.

"That's great, Annie." I had made a small difference in Annie's life and was only beginning to realize the difference she made in mine. Without hesitation, I stretched my arms and hugged her small bony shoulders.

We talked about her diet on one of the home visits. It wasn't a talk about a textbook diet, as a supply of fresh fruits and vegetables was out of reach in her situation. Annie did most of the talking and I listened. She told me about purchasing groceries with food stamps. Bacon grease was a favorite seasoning and her meals consisted of potatoes, commodity cheese and canned vegetables. A loaf of bread lasted for more than a month. She split open the wrapper and dried the bread to keep it from getting moldy. There was an advantage Annie she had over many diabetics, however. Her budget didn't allow high carbohydrate desserts, such as cakes and cookies.

Annie had learned to manage her disease, despite age and a dilapidated environment. The house remained dirty, cluttered and unkempt, with one exception: the space where she kept her diabetic supplies was pristine. On a shelf near the table, she placed a metal cake pan with the needles, syringes, cotton balls and a bottle of rubbing alcohol. This was covered with a tea towel. It was the sole clean oasis in the shabby living area.

My respect for Annie grew through the days I worked with her. She taught me to look beyond the environment to find and value the human being. My work with Annie blew away my early

bias that the appearance of a home represents the true worth of

the resident inside. I no longer feared walking through a

neighborhood where knee-high grass covered the ground. Annie

taught me to listen, to avoid judging a person by outward

appearance.

Three months later, on a Saturday morning, I heard a local

radio news broadcast while eating breakfast. A fire destroyed a

small home and displaced two elderly residents. My appetite

vanished when the names was broadcast. Annie and her male

friend were listed as the fire refugees, who were temporarily

housed in the Oak Arms Hotel. Within minutes, I arrived at the

Oak Arms Hotel and found Annie's physician standing at the

registration desk. We had both come to find Annie and make sure

she had insulin and food, at least through the weekend. In that

instance, I knew that Annie's lessons would reverberate forever.

Hills of Wonder

Tucked away behind the cornfields of my suburban Iowa college town is a dirt road that winds up the hill to a cluster of trailers and dug-out homes. As the new public health nurse, I was charged with following up on the school's complaint of multiple absences with a twelve-year old boy who lived in this area. Checking the map to confirm the address, I drove my silver-grey 50's Volkswagen up the dirt road, over ruts and around trees. The fall crisp air greeted me as I rolled windows down and looked around.

Stepping out of my car, I noticed a small low-lying shack with a cow grazing in the front yard. Off to the other side was a small faded green trailer house with a noticeable lean to one side. Just ahead at about fifty yards was an entrance to a cave-like structure on the side of a small hill. Shrugging my shoulders, I grabbed my nursing bag and opened the car door. A cluster of chickens ran from the path as I walked toward the grey shack.

"Hello," I ventured in a feeble voice.

"Well, golly-be!" replied a middle-aged stout woman with a kerchief on her head, walking toward the house with a silver a pail in one hand. "Just milked the cow...come inside," she commanded, gesturing toward the door. I followed the woman, noticing the brown cotton dress that hung under a grey cardigan oversized sweater she wore.

The doorway entrance required that I stooped to enter, despite my five-foot-three height. Heat enveloped me, and my eyes adjusted to the dim light from one cloudy window in the small room. Looking around the room, I noticed a thin elderly woman, with matted grey hair, arms crossed over her frame, humming and rocking in a wooden chair on one side of the room.

"That's Mattie," said my host with a grin. "She's there all day and only gets up when she needs more chew". I noticed that Mattie's hollow face was concave, as though she had no teeth.

She was gazing into space, seeming oblivious to my entrance.

"Just find a seat, miss." She introduced herself as "Mother Mackey" and I learned that she was the matriarch of the homes in this hillside. Mrs. Mackey and her husband moved to the area from the hills of Arkansas to find work, bringing his sister (Mattie) to live with them. Mr. Mackey found employment with the laundry room of Oakdale Hospital, a place for treatment of tuberculosis patients during the years before discovery of targeted medications. Oakdale was a distance of about five miles from this location, a distance Mr. Mackey walked to work every day, until he dug the dirt road and earned money to buy a used Ford truck.

Across the street from the Mackey home was a thirty-foot trailer where their daughter, Opal, lived with her burley husband and three-year old baby girl. Opal was pregnant with a second child and just beginning to "show". I learned that the toddler was still breast-feeding and wondered about the nutritional drain on Opal's body with two lives dependent on her for growth.

Looking around to find a wooden chair to sit, I noticed a mouse creeping across the floor. Within minutes, a large grey cat snatched the mouse and ate the head of it's prey. "Just like they all do...save the tail for a toothpick," Mrs. Mackey chuckled. It was all I could do to sit still and not run out the door.

My head spun with thoughts of how to approach the truancy issue, knowing that my supervisor would demand answers. As a new college graduate, the county hired me to perform public health tasks. Somehow, the textbooks and school experiences hadn't prepared me for this challenge. Plunging ahead, I asked for the names of the children who are school age? I learned that Jesse was twelve and in the sixth grade of Coralville Public School, while Rebecca had just entered first grade. The school-bus transported the children to school, meeting them at the bottom of the hill. When the weather turned rainy or snow banks impeded the walk, the children stayed home. With cooler temperatures and over three absences in a month, they sent me to follow up with the Mackey family.

"What keeps the children from meeting the bus?" I asked.

Mother Mackey looked at the floor before replying, "it's purty darn hard to walk through the rain and mud to get down the hill. They ain't sick. Nothin like that, miss." She looked at me and shook her head.

"You know the school and I want Jesse and Rebecca to have the best," I offered. Reminding Mrs. Mackey that public school was their privilege and Iowa law, I agreed to walk the route with Jesse and Rebecca on the next weather-challenging day. "If I can walk up to go with them down the hill," they won't need to be late or absent. To my amazement, Mrs. Mackey agreed. As I left their home, I wondered about my side of the bargain.

My thoughts wandered to the small trailer where Opal and her toddler lived. I promised to myself to return and spend time with Opal and her pregnancy questions, yet my heart pounded with anticipation and doubt.

My years of working with the Mackey clan taught me of family values and pride. It became clear that the women of the group gravitated to the Mackey house when my car arrived on the yard. They introduced me to Mrs. Woodle, a sixty-three-year old lady who was a friend from the "Hills" and lived in a shelter dug into the hillside by her young, mentally retarded older son who lived with her. She survived on county food stamps and "whatever Pete is lucky to bring home from his fishing or hunting trips." Her favorite was racoon stew that she bolstered with garden potatoes. I met the Mackey's youngest married daughter – Bella, who had two toddlers and worried about becoming pregnant with a third child.

My role as public health nurse involved providing health education, recommending health exams and vaccinations for school children and making certain school absences were less. The women and mothers of the community seemed to be a natural vehicle for the education. I suggested the plan for a monthly "Womens Club", where we gathered for socialization and health education. It was decided that the first such meeting would be at the Woodle's house on an sunny afternoon. Mother Mackey agreed to make sure everyone would be there. This would be an adventure; I mused on the opportunity to build a trusting relationship with the mothers.

The first "Hill Women's Club" day arrived and I drove my VW to the top of the hill, loaded with brochures on simple nutritional information. Mrs. Woodle invited me to join the six women in a small room, lit by a single electric light bulb hanging from the ceiling. She offered a empty glass jelly jar of Kool-Aid as refreshment, that I sipped during the meeting. After introductions, I handed out the brochures and talked about daily nutrition. I learned that the community cow provided ample milk for the children, while the rest survived on well water. The Mackey garden provided vegetables, while food stamps were used to purchase fruits. Protein was lacking in most diets, until men went fishing or hunting.

My role as public health nurse gave me access to link the Hill community children to services of the University Dental Clinic. A dental exam of the children was arranged and a school bus delivered the ten children for exams. To my surprise, there were no cavities in any of the teeth of the Hill children, despite their lack of toothbrushes and toothpaste. I realized that candy and other refined sugars were not in abundance with these beautiful children.

Opal started to wear looser clothes, trying to hide her pregnant size from straining zippers on her pants. She was interested in knowing more about the changes in her body, so I brought a visual drawing to show the normal growth of a fetus. On my second visit, Opal's her three-year old jumped on her lap, pulled her breast out for feeding. I wondered about the drain on Opal's body, noting dark circles under her eyes. We talked about the need to teach three-year old Macy to drink from a cup. I brought a pink toddler cup along as incentive. On my next visit, Opal hugged me and said that Macy gave up the breast, with, "a fly landed on my tit and I told Macy that the bug got her ditty".

****

Thirty years later, I drive past the area to find where my Hill

friends lived and find only cement roads and two-story homes.

Gone are the woods where the men hunted for meat or fished for

sustenance. Freshly-manicured green lawns, carefully laid out like

checkerboards replace fields of grasses where cows roamed. All

that is left are my memories of a community that taught me the

value of togetherness, despite all odds.

6 HOMECOMING

Martin Scott, retired policeman, packed up jars of old coins, rings and other trinkets to clear space. His prized collection came from years of scanning Rockaway Beach with a metal detector. Relocating the jars to an upstairs linen closet made the room for her medical paraphernalia. Josie was coming home, and he had to be ready. Her stroke was severe. She couldn't swallow, her speech was hard to understand, and her left side lay limp as a newborn babe. Doctors warned him that she would need around-the-clock help.

"Your wife can't eat or drink," the hospital nurse had told him. "She must be fed through this tube that goes directly into her stomach." Martin watched as the chalky nutritional solution drained into Josie's stomach from a feeding syringe.

He shifted his weight from one foot to the other, eyes blinking rapidly. "Josie will be fine with me," he said. "We have been together for over forty years, just the two of us." He clasped

Josie's good hand and wondered about that bold statement. What does an old cop know about bathing, dressing and feeding someone like Josie?

They insisted he attend case conferences where they listed Josie's disabilities in medical terms too difficult to understand. Martin listened like a convicted felon hearing a jury's verdict, his lined face blank and grey eyes fixed. The nurses swished past him, never offering words of encouragement. He was given her discharge instructions, prescriptions and referral information. Josie's medical equipment would be delivered before she arrived home.

Martin's fingers ran along the top of the hospital bed side-rail, which was set up in the center of their small living room. Cases of liquid nutritional feedings were stacked near the foot of the bed. On the opposite side of the room were two reclining chairs, his brown leather, her's teal brocade upholstered. Between the chairs was a small end table with their favorite cribbage board poised as if waiting for players.

Martin walked to the living room bay window and gazed at the empty street. A gust of wind swirled the last of autumn leaves lying on the cracked sidewalk. His wire-rimmed glasses were smudged. He cleaned them using the bottom of his red plaid flannel shirt.

A white van, with *Care Transport* in bold lettering, rounded the corner and parked at the curb. Two burly male attendants stepped out and opened the rear of the vehicle. Martin watched as they lifted Josie on a gurney and rolled her toward the front door. Her grey hair splayed on the pillow, blue eyes wide, blinking nervously. He winced as he looked at Josie's pale face and drooping lip.

"This is Josie's feeding tool," Linda said. She handed Martin a large syringe that looked like the basting device used for a Thanksgiving turkey. It felt cold and foreign in his stubby hands. Linda Van Meer was the home health nurse assigned to teach Martin the techniques for his wife's care. She demonstrated the routine of pouring the canned nutrition into the syringe. The liquid slowly funneled into Josie's stomach through a red rubber tube.

"Josie needs a can of this every four hours when she is awake."

Martin nodded. He rubbed his sweaty palms on his thighs and surveyed the feeding equipment lying on top of the bookcase. So much to remember. The dull ache in the back of his neck had returned. He tried to ignore the pain and concentrate on Linda's instructions. Overnight, their comfortable home had been transformed into a miniature hospital room. Josie's liquid medications were lined up like spices on the pantry shelf.

Martin sensed a warm glow inside knowing Josie was home. They had met at a neighborhood bar and became instant soulmates, marrying just a month later. Theirs was a good union. Martin worked with the police department, assigned to street patrols during his fifty-year career. Josephine was a librarian at the reference desk.

"No children?" Linda was completing admission forms.

"It's always been just Josie and me." Martin reached over to stroke Josie's arm. "Guess we were lucky to meet, that night in Cambert's Bar. She moved here to attend college, had a job at the library. My shift with the police was over for the day, and I stopped to relax."

"You've been together a long time." Linda looked over the top of her horn-rimmed glasses.

"You got it. Married forty-five years in July".

"Martin, here's a list of Josie's medications and the times for each. Give her a few ounces of water after each medication. Just enough to make sure all the medication gets into her stomach." Linda smiled and folded the completed paperwork.

Martin nodded and placed the medication list on the chest. "I'll do my best."

"I'll be back tomorrow to check Josie out and answer questions." Linda straightened the covers on Josie's bed. "One of our aides can come to help Josie bathe, get dressed."

Martin looked at Josie. They always made decisions together, that is...before everything changed.

We will make it alone, no help," he said in a low voice. "Josie would do the same for me, if I was the one in the chair." Martin swallowed, his back stiffened.

"Okay, you can change your mind later. Let me help you make Josie comfortable in bed." Martin watched as Linda smoothly transferred Josie to the hospital bed. He moved the wheelchair to the side of the room. Linda gathered her nursing equipment. "See you in the morning. And don't forget to call the agency if you have any questions." She placed a brochure on a table near the door and left.

They were alone. Martin listened to sounds of tree branches tapping against the windows with the wind. A relentless knocking as if something was sending him a warning using Morse code. He pulled the drapes closed to shut off the outside view. A lifetime of being alone with Josie, but this was different. The quiet was deafening. Before her stroke, Josie brought life to the house with her singing, her conversation, her laughter. The doctors said that her brain's speech center was damaged with the stroke. Martin strained to remember the sound of her voice, now gone forever. He looked around the small living-room, transformed to a make-shift hospital room. Indentations remained on the blue carpet where the sofa had been.

Martin turned on the radio and tuned to a favorite station. Soft jazz soon filled the empty spaces in the room. For him, it didn't matter that she couldn't hum to the music. Just having Josie home made him feel secure and whole.

Martin mentally went through the routines practiced at the hospital before Josie came home. Transferring her to the commode and into bed. Helping her dress in pajamas. The years of walking beaches looking for coins left him with strength for this new job. But, the feeding routine for Josie was what worried him.

Pulling out the list of instructions that Linda left, he prepared for her next feeding. Clean the top of the can, attach the syringe to her feeding tube, and pour. Seemed simple enough. "We will be okay, won't we Josie?" Martin pressed his lips to Josie's right hand. "Boy, did I ever miss having you here."

Martin awoke to the sounds of loud knocking on the front door. Sunlight was pouring around the brocade bedroom drapes. He grabbed a robe, pushed his feet into slippers and stumbled toward the living room. Josie was sleeping, her mouth open. The stale room air smelled like moldy bread. His pace quickened toward the persistent knocking on the door.

"Good afternoon, Martin." It was Linda. "How are you and Josie today?

"Come in," he stepped aside as she entered the room.

Linda walked to Josie's bedside, placing her bag on the chest near the feeding equipment. She pulled out a stethoscope and blood pressure cuff. "Going to check her vitals," she said.

Martin studied her face as she completed the exam. "Everything okay?"

"Josie, can you squeeze my hand?" Linda repeated the question in a louder voice. "She seems groggy today. Did the morning feeding go okay?"

Martin glanced at the clock. Two o'clock in the afternoon. Josie made no sounds during the night. He must have slept very soundly, and so did Josie.

"Haven't given her the feeding. Was about to do that when you came." He ran a hand over his head, to smooth his hair.

"What about her medications?" Linda's questions continued. The tone of her voice was louder, more demanding. Her eyes widened and stared at his face, the look he had seen in the face of a prosecuting attorney.

Martin wanted to tell her the truth, that he had been sleeping. Josie hadn't had her feeding, hadn't been given her liquid medications, hadn't been toileted. He wanted to be honest.

All his life he had been honest. Cops were always honest and trusted. This time was different. His ears burned, face flushed and he smiled.

"She had her medications. Time just slipped away from me, I guess. Need to give her the feeding." He picked up the Ensure can, fingers trembling.

"Good. I'll just watch to see how it goes," she said.

Martin connected the syringe to the red tube from Josie's abdomen. He opened a can of liquid nutrition and quickly poured, spilling it over the top of the syringe and down on Josie's pajamas. He saw her face grimace when the wet reached her skin.

"Oh, no. What a mess I made." He pulled a red handkerchief from his pocket to dab at the pale puddle on Josie's stomach.

"Slow down, Martin," Linda advised. She held the syringe in a vertical position while he poured the remainder of the can into the vessel. "Josie's feedings are super important. It's her life-line.

You can manage. Go slowly. Relax."

They talked in the kitchen, later, after helping Josie into clean pajamas. Linda had transferred Josie to a wheelchair. Martin rolled it to the front window. He placed a shawl around her shoulders, gently squeezing her arms in a hug.

"Her blood pressure is a little low today. And, she seems groggy, not as responsive. Maybe it's nothing to worry about. I'll speak with her doctor today, and let you know what he says."

Martin wiped his mouth, his eyes falling on the half-empty bottle of vodka on the kitchen counter. Vodka martinis were Josie's favorite. It was a ritual they shared for years: vodka martini before dinner and brandy after. Josie always insisted on chilled glasses and candles on the dinner table. He longed for the time when she could sip her martini from her favorite Waterford glass.

Linda reviewed the medication list with Martin, repeating one-by-one the times to give each dose. His mind wandered to a time seven years ago when his wrist was broken. Josie took good care of him. She helped button his shirts, even shave his whiskers when his left arm was in a cast. He needed to return the promise and care for her, do those things she could no longer do for herself.

"Looks like I need to check on Josie again. Be sure to follow all the correct times for her feedings and meds, Martin. I will be here in the morning," Linda said.

"Right. We will be here." Martin moistened his lips. His mouth tasted like rotten eggs.

"Are you the vodka drinker?" she asked.

There was no reason to ignore her question. Martin nodded and told Linda about his vodka martinis. "Josie always said I made better martinis than the bartenders in Cambert's bar."

"Josie liked martinis?"

"She looked forward to a smooth drink before dinner. Said it relaxed her. We always did it up right, candles and the works.

The martinis are her favorite."

"And your favorite?"

"Guess it would be the drinks after dinner. Brandy or aperitif. Something to settle the stomach. We loved to talk while sipping brandy around the fireplace." Martin's face glowed as he talked. "So good to have Josie back, missed her."

"Martin," Linda began, "have you been giving vodka to Josie?"

He shifted his weight from one foot to the other. "Some," he replied. "Not a good idea." Linda's voice was stern. "Why would you do that?"

"She seemed to relax. It was only a thimble full, just before the liquid stuff...last night. She slept so well."

Linda leaned back on the kitchen counter. "So, that may be why she seems groggy today. I really don't think your doctor would want you to give Josie alcohol."

Martin nodded. "Probably not... probably wasn't a good idea. Josie seemed to relax, that's all. It was almost like the old days."

"But, Martin...Josie isn't the same as she was. Please, no alcohol for Josie."

"Didn't give her to drink...just through the tube." Martin rested his arm on the counter, leaning toward Linda. His bent frame towered over the petite nurse, his red-rimmed eyes filled with tears.

"She won't ever be the same Josie as before her stroke, Martin. You can't give her anything but the cans of Ensure, water and her medications." Linda's finger pointed for emphasis, like a mother scolding a child.

"Yes, understood," said Martin. *Aye, aye sergeant,* he thought. All those years on the police force taught me how to *say* I agree with orders, even when I don't. Josie will get her feedings and medications. We'll see about the rest.

Linda gathered her papers. "Josie is on medication to control her blood pressure. Alcohol mixed with blood pressure meds could be dangerous, could drop her blood pressure too low, could slow her breathing."

Martin glanced at Josie's frame in front of the window. She was a shell of the person he married, but still beautiful. He felt his stomach cramp with an empty lost feeling. Martin followed Linda to the front door. She carried her bag and papers.

"Our social worker may have some suggestions for additional help. I'll see if she can schedule you in tomorrow. Her name is Loretta."

Josie sat in her wheelchair, head nodding slightly. She smiled, that crooked lip smile, when Martin returned to the room. "Little bit cold, Josie?" He tucked a blue knit afghan around her legs. Linda news worried him. He never meant to hurt Josie, just gave her the vodka to relax. Just like in the old days. A little vodka to relax never hurt anyone, Josie always said. She usually had the martini glasses chilled when he came home from walking the beat. She loved the cocktails before dinner, said it made the stress of the day disappear.

The noise of someone banging on the front door startled Martin from a sound sleep. He realized that he had fallen asleep in the reclining chair next to Josie's bed. Must have slept there all night. Was still dressed in his plaid shirt and wrinkled work pants.

"Coming...hold on, I'm coming." He rubbed his eyes and glanced at his face in the mirror. Where was the old face, he wondered, as he looked at the ghost-like reflection. His thick grey mane of hair stuck out in all directions. He wiped his hands on his pants and opened the door.

"Mr. Scott? Good afternoon. Linda asked me to see you." A middle-aged, plump lady with brown hair pulled into a bun held out her hand.

Martin shook the woman's hand. "Sorry it took me time to get to the door. Was busy with my Josie."

"Yes, she takes time. I'm Loretta, your social worker. Can I come in?"

"Oh, sure. Come in." He ushered her into the living room, opening heavy drapes. The mid-day sun illuminated dust layered on the table tops. Josie would be embarrassed, he thought. She always kept a neat house, organized like the books on her library reference desk.

"Tried to call you, Mr. Scott. Your phone rang and rang...were you out?" Loretta walked slowly toward Josie's bed. She looked around the room, as if making a mental recording for evidence.

"Sometimes I don't hear the phone." Martin felt his ears burn. *None of her business,* he thought, responding to her accusatory tone of voice.

"Well, I was worried," Loretta slipped her coat off and hung it over the back of the blue reclining chair. She moved a pile of newspapers and placed her bag on an end table. As she approached Josie's bed, Loretta's foot bumped an empty vodka bottle and it rolled away. She touched Josie's shoulder. A faint odor of urine wafted from her sheets.

"My job is to connect you with resources. Josie needs lots of attention and care. Perhaps I can find some help for you. Church volunteers, and the like."

"No...Josie and I are doing fine," Martin said. *Another do-gooder. Smile, be polite and she will leave.*

"There are community resources, some for little or no cost," Loretta said.

"Appreciate the interest, but we will be all right." Martin pulled the sheet to cover a stain on Josie's flannel nightgown.

"Can we review her medications, Martin?" Loretta pulled a list of medicines from the home health folder left by the nurse. "What have you given her today?"

Martin rubbed his face, the whiskers made a scratchy noise

against his hand. The rhythmic tick of a wall clock seemed deafening in the silence. Loretta was waiting for an answer. Her face carried a no-nonsense expression.

"Can't say…guess I didn't write it down," he said.

Loretta paused, her hands on her hips. She looked at Martin's bloodshot eyes, wrinkled face and slight hand tremor. "Linda and I are worried about Josie. She needs feedings and medications on a schedule, Martin." She folded her arms like a drill sergeant and stared.

"Don't you think I know that?" Martin felt like a truant boy.

"This is a heroic task you are trying to do. Josie needs more care than it is possible for you. All the bathing, toileting, feeding is too much work."

"That's your opinion, lady." Martin voice was shaky. He swallowed to clear the lump in his throat.

"Martin, it's my job to report situations where someone

could be in danger. Someone, like Josie, who can't protect

herself." Loretta pulled a pen from her bag and began writing.

"What are you saying?" He shifted his weight as if to keep

from losing balance. He ran a hand over his messy mane of hair.

"I have to contact Adult Protective Services. Part of my job.

Someone will be coming here to investigate." Loretta turned and

placed her notes into her leather bag. She closed it with a snap.

"What for?" Martin heard the noise of cars driving through

the slush on the street outside. The sunlight through stained glass

windows cast a cold light across the hospital bed.

"The caseworker from Adult Protective will review Josie's

case. If she believes that she is in danger, she will find a nursing

home for Josie."

"What? Nursing Home? No way. You can't take Josie

away from me." Martin stiffened his arms, fists clenched. His face

flushed beet red.

"Martin, we are only doing what's right for Josie."

"Right? What do you know about what's right for us?" His eyes narrowed and jaws clenched. "Josie and I are okay...don't need anyone." Martin's voice was low and steady.

Loretta placed her hand on his shoulder. "You have done your best, and we know how hard it is to be twenty-four hour caregiver. Why don't you let me send someone to help? If this doesn't ease the load, you can cancel."

Martin hung his head. What would hurt, he thought. He nodded. Loretta smiled, folded her coat over her arm, closed her bag and left. He watched her drive away, tears welled in his eyes. Losing Josie would be like death. She was his only reason for being. He walked to her bedside and stroked her face.

7 ANGST OF AGING

I knew there was trouble when I heard the breathing before the door opened. Sounded like air blowing through a straw in a glass of water. My neck muscles tightened as I looked into the red-rimmed eyes of the elderly man at the door. His ruddy face with several days-old-stubble carried a pained expression. Dressed in wrinkled clothes that looked clean, his plaid shirt collar was frayed and he had an odor of decaying sweat. He stood just inside the doorway, peering at me from under a frown, panting breaths making greetings impossible.

"Your son-in-law, Bruce, called and asked me to come. I'm a nurse," I said, pointing to an identification badge clipped to my blue jacket. He nodded and motioned for me to follow him. The cluttered living room air was stale and damp, like entering a tomb. Drapes were closed over windows. A small ceramic table lamp cast a dim glow near the doorway.

The long-distance phone call from Bruce Mason had come after hours for the home health office. My work was finished for the week, and I was headed home. Maybe it was the fear in Bruce's voice that had sent a chill like icicles down my back and caused me to agree.

Mr. Fedele sat at the edge of a small couch just inside the living room. On a nearby table was an array of prescription bottles with cardiac medications that I recognized: Lanoxin, Lasix, Potassium Chloride. Placing my bag on the floor, I sat at the opposite end of the couch. His shoulders seemed to rise and fall with each breath as if every muscle strained to pull in air. Veins in his neck bulged, and I noticed perspiration on his forehead. No need for a stethoscope to see he was critically ill.

"How long have you been breathing like this?" I asked before realizing the impossibility of taking a medical history. He merely shook his head and mouthed something that looked like "today."

"You need emergency medical help, Mr. Fedele. Let me

call your doctor." I reached into my bag and pulled out a cell phone and a ballpoint pen. He opened the table drawer, retrieved a gray address book with a business card paper-clipped to the front cover, and handed it to me. The card was well worn around the edges: Dr. Gilbert Adams, Family Physician.

As I dialed the number, my eyes swept the dimly lit room. Then I saw her sitting on an upholstered chair across the room silently staring into space, her bony frame dressed in a flowered housedress, now several sizes too large, hands clutching the edge of a knitted afghan on her lap like a child holding a favorite blanket. Her feet were enclosed in purple slippers that matched the veins on her bare ankles.

"Mr. Fedele," I said while waiting for the phone call connection. "Your doctor may want you to go to the hospital."

"No, no, can't leave Millie," he said, shaking his head. He glanced at the elderly lady sitting across the room and wiped his mouth. "Won't leave Millie alone," he whispered.

Millie began to rock back and forth on the couch, making chewing motions with her mouth.   Dr. Adams answered the phone on the first ring. "This is Marie Henson," I said. "I'm with your patient, Joseph Fedele. He has dyspnea, breath sounds are full of moist rales, and his skin is ashen grey."

"Hmm...well, Joe has a history of severe congestive heart failure. He needs to get to the E. R., I'll meet him there."

"But, doctor, he's worried about Millie..."

"Marie, he needs emergency medical care. Get him to the hospital...or he may die."

"I'll call for an ambulance," I said, closing the cell phone.

Joe began to cough, his body convulsing with each expiration. I felt my stomach knot and counted the seconds between each breath he took. Millie looked at me with vacant grey eyes. Her tiny frame seemed lost in her clothes, scrawny elbows sticking out of sleeves, hands lifeless in her lap, a small gold band visible on her finger.

"Joe, I'll stay with Millie," I said impulsively. Anything to get him off to the hospital emergency room, and not to die on my watch. This seemed to be the only option.

My hand reached out to touch his shoulder as he looked into my face and continued to shake his head. His breath carried a sickening odor like rancid fruit.

"You're struggling to breathe, Joe. Dr. Adams believes it's congestive heart failure, like you've had before. He'll meet you at the E.R.," I said.

Across the room, Millie mumbled something incoherent like a babbling child. She shifted the afghan on her lap, crossed her legs and continued the rocking.

"Millie needs you to be well, Joe," I said quietly. Light from a streetlight filtered around the drapes creating shadows on the worn carpet. My mind rehearsed the motions of cardio-pulmonary resuscitation, praying it wouldn't be needed.

Joe hung his head, closed his eyes and shrugged his shoulders, then nodded to me. I went to work calling the emergency service and giving them directions. The next phone call was to Bruce in Massachusetts explaining what was happening. He sighed as I continued. "Right now, I'll stay with your mother until I can find an aide to stay around the clock."

"Yes, yes, of course. Whatever it takes," he said.

Joe stood, using the chair for support, and slowly made his way to a small oak bureau at the side of the room. From it, he pulled his wallet, stuffing it into his pocket and rearranging papers, before locking the top drawer. His eyes scanned the room as though memorizing the scene.

"Does Millie take any medicines, Joe?"

"No, she's good...cept for her mind." Using furniture for support, Joe ambled over to Millie and mumbled something, leaning over to hug her shoulders. She smiled, unaware of the commotion in the room. His shoulders hung down in resignation.

There was a knock on the door. I opened it to let two male emergency medics enter. They placed a portable oxygen mask over Joe's face before loading him on to a gurney. He grasped my hand, eyes filling with tears, before being carried out the front door.

The chime of a grandfather clock interrupted the sudden silence of the room. Six o'clock, Friday night, and that nagging ache in my back returned. I walked to sit next to Millie, moving a pile of newspapers. She continued to rock gently, holding her arms in a self-hug. A faint odor of urine kept me from getting too close.

"Millie, it's you and me for a while." She tilted her head and looked at me. Pulling a phone list of home health aides from my briefcase, I started making calls. No answer to the first three numbers on my list. Working from the top of the list to the bottom, one by one, names were crossed off. Friday night is the worst time to find an available aide.

On the fourth call, a female voice answered, "No habla Ingles." My Spanish is poor and, much as I tried, we could not communicate. The only other possible option, I thought, was to take Millie home with me. If I didn't find an aide within the next fifteen minutes, I would have to take Millie to my house: Plan B, I thought. The bizarre idea of Millie spending the weekend in my apartment seemed surreal.

There were only two names left on my list, and three minutes left on my arbitrary time limit before moving to Plan B. Dialing Addie Johnson's phone number, I said a silent prayer.

"Addie, this is Marie and I need your help," I said. I explained the situation, realizing that my words tumbled out like water over a dam. Addie is a favorite aide with years of experience. She agreed to help and could stay until Monday morning, if needed.

Closing the cell phone and putting the phone list back into my briefcase, I turned to Millie. "Let me find you some supper," I said. She looked at me with a faint smile and I noticed remnants of dried food on her bodice.

I walked into the narrow kitchen just off the dining area, finding a light switch just inside the doorway. The smell of garbage met me from the overflowing trashcan, soiled dishes piled in the sink. A coffeepot with remnants of morning brew sat on a linoleum countertop. I opened the yellow refrigerator door to a white plastic bowl of soup, congealed fat clumps floating on top. A quick sniff and I judged that it was not spoiled. A half-full bottle of milk and a bagel half occupied another shelf.

The mystery soup it is, I thought, pulling the bowl out and placing it on the counter. Searching through a cupboard, I found a pot and, before long, the aroma of chicken vegetable soup filled the small kitchen. I dug through the pile of dishes to find a medium-sized bowl, washed it and ladled soup for Millie's supper.

Bringing the soup bowl to the table, I motioned to Millie. "Come, have some soup, Millie." She stood as if unfolding in slow motion, and shuffled to sit at the table. I watched her hungrily spoon the soup into her mouth. Dribbles ran down her chin to the soiled front of her dress. The noise of raindrops against the window signaled that the typical late day storm had arrived.

Within a few minutes, the doorbell rang announcing Addie's arrival. "You're an angel," I said as she removed her sweater and put her overnight bag down. I introduced her to Millie and gave her instructions.

"Just do your magic, Addie," I said. "Millie looks hungry, but I couldn't find much in the cupboards or refrig. She needs a bath and shampoo. I haven't looked around."

Addie greeted Millie and both looked to be at ease. "I'll be here in the morning, Addie, to bring some groceries and see how things are. Call me if anything comes up." On my way home, I called Bruce to give him an update on his in-laws condition.

Early the next morning, I phoned the emergency room and learned Mr. Fedele was admitted for a short hospital stay. When I arrived at the Fedele house, Addie met me at the door. Millie had

a shower, shampoo and was dressed in clean clothes. Overnight,

Addie had returned this home to order and peace.

8 BREAST CANCER CONUNDRUM

Breast Cancer Conundrum

"It scared me when they said another round of chemo failed," remarks Carol, who has been battling metastatic breast cancer for over eighteen years. I gaze into the face of a frail, seventy-year-old woman who has endured surgery, received chemotherapy and radiation with many side effects. She has lost over twenty pounds, felt her strength decline and developed neuropathy in her fingers and feet. Her passion for dog agility waned because of her inability to train her beloved Papillion. Carol's eyes echo the grey mist hanging over the lake outside our backdoor. I notice the way her pants bag from weight loss, her slow steps to the chair where she folds as in resignation.

Carol's first noticed a lump in her breast nine years ago. She had a total resection of her breasts, followed by a course of chemotherapy. During the recovery phase, she lost hair and suffered excruciating pain. Her strength returned and she returned to teaching at a local school. With time, she learned to paddle board and began a hobby of dog agility competition.

Nine years after breast surgery, Carol noticed pain in her arm, which she attributed to paddle boarding. The pain didn't disappear with rest and physicians noticed tumor growth in her bones. Her oncologist recommended a new chemotherapy regimen. Medical tests suggested a need for a body scan where metastatic lesions were found in her bones, lung and liver. The femur appeared weakest on scan, so she agreed to insertion of a rod for support. Her hair loss and discomfort did not slow her daily walks with Papillion Cody.

Just two years later, despite oral chemotherapy and following a rigid plan of diet and exercise, Carol presented with an annoying cough and hoarse voice caused by a tumor growth on her cervical spine. Physicians recommended another course of radiation, pinpointed toward the intruding mass. A third recurrence appeared with signs of lung mass growth. She began treatment with a different chemotherapy, followed by the usual side effects of hair loss and a numbness in fingers. I watched my friend and neighbor decline in strength and courage, and felt helpless.

On a recent medical visit, I volunteered to drive Carol to her weekly appointment for labs and hydration. We motor north to a five-story building where I found a wheelchair while she waited on a first-floor bench. With the wheelchair, I push her on the elevator to the second-floor treatment center. A nurse assists Carol to a reclining chair with an attached infusion pole. I look at the drawn faces of men and women receiving chemotherapy or hydration infusion therapy. One twenty-some girl with a rounded face and stocking cap looked at me with questions written on her pale face. An African-American man shuffled to sit in a recliner next to Carol, hunching forward and placing his hands over his face. The floor-to-ceiling windows behind the patient chairs look out over a wooded area. Trees are gently blowing in the breeze with green grass covering the ground. All patient recliners are placed with backs against the windows, restricting the view for patients. This seems incongruous to me but perhaps the positive view of sunshine and green grass conflicts with emotions of the patients?

Breast cancer research continues to nibble away at the edges of a cure, yet there are still no answers. Is submitting to surgery, chemotherapy and radiation treatments worth the hope of living another or week, or month? Is the enormous financial burden of a treatment that forces families into bankruptcy and poverty worth the endless struggle? These are individual decisions not easily answered. If I faced such questions, what would I decide?

The cancer patient is not the only individual affected by the disease. Family members experience the need to change plans as the health of their significant other impacts everything from career choices to retirement and vacation plans. Carol and her husband planned a trip to Hawaii set for just after her retirement from a school teaching position. They consulted maps, airfare and hotel expenses were determined and placed on reserve. The initial mammography result and breast biopsy dashed their dreams of the vacation. Carol was scheduled for breast surgery, while vacation maps were thrown in the recycling bins to be hauled away.

Modern-day health care professionals advocate patient informed choice with treatment options. The potential benefit risks/side effects of treatment options are often explained in a rushed manner. Such information comes in a quick verbal overview by a member of the oncologist's team, before a request to sign a consent. Sometimes a shining brochure from a pharmaceutical firm is used. Smiling faces appear on the cover, while facts, written in small font follow. To hear medical facts and read drug information may be worthless. Data is often presented with language not understood by the lay public. Compounding this dilemma is the underlying stress that clouds the patient's decision.

Palliative care is an option that is gaining recognition among health care professionals and lay audiences. This multidisciplinary approach focuses on the patient's unique goals for life and works to provide quality of life within those boundaries. Support for patient choices emphasizes the role of the patient in his/her stage of life. Care interventions may include pain control, along with stress management techniques and emotional/spiritual support. Unlike hospice care that focuses on end-of-life care, the palliative care patient receives continued medical treatment and support from the initial diagnosis toward remission. This holistic approach to care of patients with severe, often chronic illnesses has resulted in improved quality of life. The palliative care focus in on patient dignity and comfort.

Carol was not offered palliative care as an adjunct to her treatment plan. When side effects of the chemo became unbearable, her oncologist offered to delay further medication for a few days. When her present chemo drug resulted in severe loss of body function, she was switched to an alternate medication with a promise of fewer problems. A new chemotherapy recipe may show promise for a week, until cancer markers show resurgence.

One of the newest cancer treatments on the market is displayed through television advertisement – showing smiling women returning to daily life. Carol's physician urged her to opt for this intravenous medication. After the initial dose, she returned home and collapsed. Her husband called for emergency help for admission to the hospital.

"It is becoming more difficult to live with this disease," she remarked to me. I listened as she showed that she may opt for refusing additional treatments. I watched her spirit for life disappear while physicians recommended another new medication, suggesting that remission was possible. Her medical insurance exhausted, and charity help had reached to a maximum limit. One of the chemo medications cost $800 for each weekly dose.

The medical community talks about a need to honor informed patient choice. When that choice goes against recommendations for additional but risky treatment, physicians often resist the patient's decisions. I wonder if Carol was given support for choosing palliative care, to live her days with little pain and struggle, the answer to her unspoken question would be clear. Would I want to continue with the almost never-ending painful side effects of the cancer treatments with little hope of cure? This question haunts me when I remember the long saga of my friend.

9 HOSPICE MEMORIES

The late-night call, your life's end near

And the goodbye would be painful.

My heart sunk like a pebble

Dropped into a stream as I

Rushed to your bedside.

Too young to die, I silently cried inside,

Too many dreams destroyed,

Helpless to stop the death march.

The dimly lit room, shallow breaths, your wasted body

Like the rotting decay of old lumber. Helpless,

I gently touched your face.

Our paths crossed when you chose hospice, and

I was assigned to your care.

How your strength for dying lingers with my soul.

We talked light-heartedly in the early days,

You teased me, requesting pizza, knowing your gut would retch.

You listened to my empty words of advice

As a child listens to a favorite teacher.

The silence closed around your final hours

As calm entered the room.

An unfilled promise left

A kaleidoscope of memories. Your body

Drenched with sweat from pain's torment,

Hollow eyes sunken, a gaunt façade.

Emaciated limbs motionless and angular at your side,

The putrid odor of death's last breaths.

Our eyes meet and linger with an unspoken bond.

With a whisper, a smile, I hear those last words,

"Did you bring pizza tonight?"

10 MISSED CLUES

It was early on a Tuesday morning when the telephone rang, interrupting the silence in the home health office. I was alone and startled by the ring that made my ears buzz. As agency director, I always arrived early to organize the day's schedule. This was a habit that allowed quiet time before the rush of the day. An early morning call could be an employee with an excuse for staying away from work: car won't start, baby sick, flu symptoms. I had heard them all. This call was unique and changed everything.

"Can you give me directions to your office?" said the male voice on the other end of the receiver.

"Who are you?" I stiffened, hand on my hip. Phone calls at this hour were rare and the voice was one that I didn't recognize.

"I'm from Immigration. Can you give me directions?"

As a South Florida newcomer, I was cautious. This wasn't small-town Iowa where everyone knew everyone. The morning light had begun to brighten the sky outside the office, the street was quiet, the parking lot vacant. I told the caller to give me his name, badge number and a telephone number so I could verify his request as legitimate. "I'll call you back after I know you are on official business," I said.

"Sure." I heard a loud sigh, "but you won't be able to reach anyone in the Miami office until after eight thirty."

"So, call me back after nine."

I hung up the telephone and glanced at the clock. It was forty-five minutes until I could reach the Miami Immigration office. That is, if the number he gave me was really the INS. I dismissed the call from my thoughts and reviewed a list of scheduled patient admissions. It looked to be a routine day, with three morning diabetics, a cardiac admission and a post surgical with wound care.

Sylvia arrived to work and waved a greeting, then walked to her desk at the front of the office. She was a reliable employee who managed aide schedules and personnel files. Her broad smile and pleasant persistence brought results. I thought about the last Friday afternoon when the hospital discharged several patients that needed weekend help. Sylvia worked late to assign every new patient, making sure there would be no mistakes. I thought about mentioning the morning phone call to her, but didn't.

I returned to my computer and opened the company e-mail. I could hear the rumble of the traffic outside the store-front office. The small agency office was in an old strip mall. Large glass windows and a door faced the parking lot out front. My office was in the back, near a small space that doubled for supplies and a lunchroom.

The front door opened. Four men and a lady walked into the office, moving together. They were dressed in worn blue jeans, plain blue or grey tee shirts, some with unbuttoned plaid shirts worn as jackets, and baseball caps. A larger, older man was ahead of the pack; he pulled a black plastic card-sized folder from his shirt pocket. He held it toward me to display an official looking gold badge. "We're from Immigration and here to arrest one of your aides," he said.

The only sound I heard was the sudden rustle of papers on Sylvia's desk. My mouth dropped open and my mind raced to think of a reply. The badge looked official, but the attire of this group was not what I expected from governmental officers. I wondered whether this was a strange hoax. "You look like you just stepped off a boat," I said. I felt a nervous twitch under my left eyelid.

The leader smiled briefly, then returned the badge to his shirt pocket. I noticed lines that crinkled around his grey eyes, the round abdomen that hung over his belt buckle, the grey hair sprinkled in with brown on his head. "We're here to arrest Guerlaine Josephs. She's here illegally." His voice was low and direct. His arms were down and away from his body, legs slightly spread. I remembered seeing that same posture on security guards outside the local bank.

"Sylvia, don't we have identification on Guerlaine?" I walked toward her desk, still uncertain about this group. At that moment, I was thinking about the steep penalties for hiring illegal immigrants and I was concerned about my job. If this was real, the agency could be faced with legal problems.

Sylvia pulled open a file drawer, her fingers paging back to Guerlaine's file. "Right here," she said, pointing to copies of identification. I trusted Sylvia. She was persistent about having complete information before anyone was hired. A poster from Immigration with details on verifying legal documentation was taped to the wall behind her desk.

"You may have something that looks legal, ma'am," the leader said. "Illegals often buy documentation. Fake documents that look legal can be purchased on many streets in Miami." As he talked, the others hung around their leader like back-up singers in a band. The girl's hair was pulled back into a ponytail and made her seem barely old enough to drive. I wondered how she became part of this group and whether she could arrest anyone.

"We need to take Miss Josephs into custody," he said, looking directly at me.

I frowned and tried to register what he said. Guerlaine was a shy, pretty Haitian aide who had been hired almost three months earlier. She spoke with a heavy accent but demonstrated kindness and care through her touch. I remembered her smile when she got her first paycheck, her brown eyes reminded me of a lost puppy. It was during a staff meeting that she called me her *ange-guardien.* I later learned that was Creole for "guardian angel".

"You must be mistaken," I said. "How can you know that the documents we have are not legal?" My arms ached as though I was swimming against a strong current.

"No mistake," he said. "She is here illegally and we have a warrant for her arrest." He held out an official form and I saw Guerlaine's name at the top.

My mouth was dry, as though I had eaten a dozen soda crackers. I leaned against a filing cabinet for support.

"Let me take them to her," said Sylvia. "She's at the hospital this morning. Maybe, she can prove this is a mistake." She gathered her purse and car keys.

I thought of the elderly couple who were Guerlaine's usual assignments. She cared for them every morning, for three weeks. Their daughter had written *Guerlaine is so good for Mom* on a note with the check she sent. Rose and Eddie depended on Guerlaine to help them bathe, dress and reminded them to take medicines. Just last week, she stayed late to comfort Rose during a noisy thunderstorm. I saw Guerlaine place her arm around an excited Rose and walk with her. Rose responded by leaning into Guerlaine as a nervous child leans into a mother for reassurance.

"Okay, I said. "I'll work to find a replacement for her assignments this morning." Surely they were looking for the wrong girl. I believed that Guerlaine could correct the confusion and life would return to normal.

Sylvia led the group toward the front door. "My car is the

blue Ford, over there," she said. The officers followed her out the door. I watched them pile into an older Dodge van and drive away.

During the next hour, the atmosphere in our office returned to a normal daily routine. Nurses came in, restocked their bags and left for home visit assignments. The fax machine came to life printing referrals from the hospital, or signed physician orders. My fingers traced down the list of home health aides to find a replacement: Ida. I called her and she agreed to take Guerlaine's morning assignments.

It was impossible for me to stay focused on my work. My mind replayed the morning event as if searching for clues for a positive ending. Until six months ago, I lived in Iowa and knew no one who was not born in this country. Most had extended family within a fifty mile radius of their homes. My small hometown was so homogenous that we had only one Jewish family and none of African-American background. I enjoyed living and working in Florida because of the diversity. My work colleagues taught me many new customs and a different cuisines. Only three of the home health aides were born in America, the others had Caribbean island backgrounds.

Two hours after she left, Sylvia returned. It was the way her jaw was set, lips pinched and her determined stride that warned me. "It was awful, simply awful," she said. She described the scene at the hospital, about bringing Guerlaine to the lobby where the Immigration Officers "grabbed her and put her in handcuffs." She said that Guerlaine's eyes filled with tears but she didn't struggle and said nothing when she was arrested. Sylvia was allowed to bring back only her personal items: a small black purse, cell phone and a Bible.

"They're taking her to a detention center in Miami." Sylvia slumped into her desk chair and put her head in her hands. "It's not right...we need to do something."

"Doesn't she have a husband?" I said. I remembered that Guerlaine requested time off to be married, several weeks earlier. The nervous look in her eyes, at that time, was something that I attributed as typical for a young bride-to-be. Now, I wasn't so sure that it was pre-wedding jitters. Was the wedding a process to make her residence here legal? The thought surfaced, but I dismissed it.

"You're right," said Sylvia. "Her husband works in the kitchen at the nursing home. I'll call him." She picked up the phone and I heard her brief conversation with Guerlaine's husband. He was Haitian and would know what to do or who to contact, I thought.

Later that afternoon, a large black man strolled into the office. He was dressed in a white short-sleeved shirt and white denim pants. He brought a fried foods aroma on his apron, tied low around his hips. "My lawyer made a mistake," he said, with a heavy Creole accent. "I'll call him and straighten this out, no problem."

Sylvia handed him Guerlaine's personal items. "Let us know what we can do to help," she said.

"Nothing for you to do. I'll fix the problem, no problem" he said. His face remained blank as he talked. It was as if he was speaking about fixing a broken chair and not his wife's predicament. "I have a good lawyer, don't worry." He left as quickly as he entered our office.

Friday was our payday and I decided to personally deliver Guerlaine's check to her husband. I wanted to learn what he was doing to obtain his wife's release. He agreed to meet me in front of the nursing home before his afternoon shift began. I waited on a bench near the front door. A black crow scolded me from the top of a nearby palm.

"Thanks for coming early to meet me," I said.

"No problem, you brought her paycheck?" He stood with arms crossed over his chest. His rotund frame towered over me.

"Yes, but first, I came because I want to know what is happening with your wife".

"It's not your business," he said. His eyes narrowed slightly and nostrils flared.

"Well, I think it is my concern," I said. "She was arrested and taken from work and I need to know that someone is working for her release. Who is your lawyer? What is happening to her?" My hand gripped the paycheck envelope. I felt beads of sweat on my upper lip.

"No, it's not your problem. Give me her paycheck. I'm going to work, now." His hand reached toward me and I stepped back a few feet. The heat of the sun matched the warm flush I felt in my face.

"Perhaps you will talk to our lawyers, if you won't talk to me," I said. It realized it was an empty threat. I could tell by the smug expression on his face that he knew this, as well.

He moved so close that I could smell the spicy scent from his skin. I saw the muscles in his arms flex, watched the slow sweeping of his eyes across my face. "No time for this, lady. Her paycheck, now."

I felt like a young girl who had crossed paths with the school bully. I held out my hand and gave him the pay envelope. He stepped toward the nursing home entrance, then turned. "Stay out of my life," he said, and disappeared inside.

As the weeks continued, Guerlaine's situation hung like a cloud over the normal mood of our office. We rarely talked about the arrest, although Sylvia called the Krome Detention Center in Miami and was informed that Guerlaine was allowed no visitors. In the evening, I searched for on-line computer reports about Krome and became more alarmed. Krome Detention was a jail with several media reports of prisoner abuse.

Sylvia's attempts to reach Guerlaine's husband went nowhere. She called daily but he rarely answered the telephone. One day he told her that he had hired another lawyer, and ranted about the money he was spending on his wife's release. Later, he stopped answering Sylvia's calls. It was as though this beautiful, young girl was pulled from our midst without any reasonable explanation.

Almost a year later, Sylvia received a phone call from the Krome Detention Center in Miami. She was told that Guerlaine had been deported back to Haiti. We never learned what happened when she returned to her home country.

I think of Guerlaine during the early morning hours, when I'm awake and can't fall back to sleep. There is an ache in my chest when I remember my silence on her arrest. Why didn't I ask more questions, seek answers? Why didn't I confront her husband instead of merely handing off the full responsibility to him? He was too calm, too unemotional and I missed the clues.

11 HEARTS FOR HAITI

Pastor Rich announced the Haiti Mission trip at the close of a Sunday morning service. My mind swirled at the prospect of visiting this foreign, third world country just a short plane ride from our South Florida home. What would the land, the people, the environment reveal to unravel a mystery that was haunting me for more than a year.

Guerlaine was a gentle, beautiful soul who was hired to join my home health team. She was soft spoken with a genuine smile. Her caring and love for the elderly made her a favorite of many patients. During a recent hurricaine, she held a frightened lady to calm her during the storm's fury. It was a surprise when my morning coffee was interrupted by a trio of immigration authorities who burst into my office, flashing official documents and stated their need to arrest her. When I protested that she was hired with proof of legal immigration status, the answer was, simply "you can get what looks legal on any street corner in Miami.

Signing on to join the mission trip to Haiti was my need to understand why Guerlaine was arrested and deported. News reports described boatloads of Haitians attempting to leave their homeland. Florida policy of "wet foot-dry foot" invited refugees to attempt dangerous ocean crossings, hoping to reach dry land. Those who were intersected during the trip were arrested and deported back to Haiti, an island nation with limited resources and reports of violence. What conditions led to people fleeing home to an unknown future?

My church provided leadership and financial support to a non-governmental school and medical clinic in a village just outside Port-au-Prince. Annual mission trips introduced parishioners to the need for support to the project. Our team of six went through preparations of: reading about the brief history of Haiti, it's artistic culture, and traditions. We checked passports, purchased air-fare tickets from Fort Lauderdale to Port-au-Prince (a two-hour flight), and packed extra toothbrushes, donated shoes and other miscellaneous items requested by full time mission staff.

My excitement peaked when Greg (who made the same trip one year earlier) approached me and advised "when leaving the airport, make sure to see the scene on the right of the vehicle". In my imagination, I envisioned a beautiful tropical paradise. Haiti was nestled in the Caribbean waters and must be full of natural beauty. What could possibly lead Guerlaine and others to attempt illegal entry into Florida?

The airplane trip was smooth. During flight, I looked out the window to a see the teal blue ocean lapping the shores of Haiti's northern shore. Typical tropical paradise, I thought. Landing in Haiti and entering the airport was a different scene. Immediately, we walked into thrust me into a crowded, chaotic room. Noise of loudspeakers of airport officials, clashed with shouts of local people trying to attract attention to their needs. Uniformed United Nations guards stood by and watched the scene. Our guide advised us to stay close, avoid the appeals of people crowing outside the fence, while keeping a tight grip on our luggage. I followed the mission guide to board a diesel flat bed truck for the forty-minute ride to our destination.

Remembering the advice from Greg, I kept my eyes trained on the scene unfolding at the right side of the truck. On the banks of a river was a large garbage pile with huge boars routing through the mess. My shock continued with a view of burning tires on each side of the road, their odor assaulting my nose. Small huts lined the road, advertising merchandise for sale – from auto parts to clothing. People were everywhere, walking or riding motor scooters – darting in and out of our way. Women walked with large containers of water balanced on their head. Horns blaring with a small colorful bus loaded with passengers, some hanging on the outside of the vehicle. Later, I learned these buses were called "Tap-Taps", because riders notified the driver to stop by tapping on the top of the cab.

Arriving at our lodging destination, our driver and guide opened gates to enter a cement enclosure where the dorm-like structures were located. Hens roamed freely outside the small building and provided a calm from the chaos outside our compound. Small palm trees and tropical vegetation surrounded the one-story structure with ten identical rooms. Each room was equipped with two bunk beds, and a small bathroom with toilet and shower. In the center of the compound was a small screened room with cement floor and table for eating meals. We learned that typical American luxuries of electricity and internet access would not be reliable. Our guide presented the agenda for the week's trip for morning visits to the mission school and medical clinic – making afternoon forays to the steel drum artists, local grocery stores and a trip to view the place where earthquake victims were buried.

Early the next morning, we were awakened by a rooster's call and made our way to the eating area for breakfast before hopping into the back of the truck to travel to the mission. The flat-bed truck had wooden benches to carry travelers to the mission compound. Driving through mud-rutted dirt roads with diesel fumes flowing over us was an adventure. Our thirty-mile drive took us through busy streets with small buildings lining our route.

Occasional piles of discarded tires seemed to be in contrast with graffiti announcing love for Jesus on the sides of Tap-Tap buses darting by. I noticed a patch of green grass near what appeared to be an intersection with a small religious statue.

Just outside the city limits, the view shifted to fields of sugar cane and distant mountains. The noise of the city dwindled and fewer people passed us in motor scooters. We arrived to the mission compound and our guards opened tall, heavy wooden gates to enter. Five or six women and children had camped just outside the gates, waiting for the clinic to open. Their faces reflected worry and despair, combined with hope for what may be inside.

Our truck was greeted with shouts and laughter of school children, running along side the truck to the school building parking space. The school building, painted coral with blue trim, announced our visit with a paper welcome banner fastened to the main wall. Just a few yards down the walk was the chapel where we would teach bible school. Inside the roofed open-side structure were child-sized benches with a small podium at the front of the room. Behind the chapel was a small restroom area, with toilets but no sink – just a steel drum full of water for rinsing hands. We learned to carry our own Kleenex to use as paper.

Haitian women teachers directed us to opening ceremonies in the courtyard, where the Haitian flag was unfurled. Each class of children lined up to sing songs, their faces glowing. As their cherubic voices rang, my heart warmed to think these beautiful children may someday fall to fates of violence or natural destruction. The school provided basic education and one meal daily to six hundred children, ages three years to eighteen. Each year, more than three hundred applications are denied because the classes are filled. Each child wears a uniform and arrives sparkling clean with smiling faces. My prayers are that this experience will enable these children to live without succumbing to multiple threats that cause people to take risky escape strategies.

Each day of our five-day visit, we watched and listened to the persistence and patience of the Haitian people, who despite earthquakes and hurricanes, although surrounded by political upheaval and violence, maintain a hope for a peaceful life. Returning to my Florida home, I am left with prayers for these neighbors who struggle for respect in a world that has often extended empty help. I find it difficult to leave a water faucet running, without thinking of the women hauling vats of water on their heads.

ANGRY PATIENTS

"Never saw a nurse worth anything," uttered the slim, elderly man with a scowl on his face. Joseph was referred to the home health agency after discharge from a three-day hospital stay for congestive heart failure. He lived alone is an assisted living facility. Dressed in denim pants that had a slept-in appearance, his uncombed grey hair matched the stubble on his face. He grumbled a quick "hello", turned away from the door and shuffled to the living room. I followed.

The room felt isolating, with drapes closed from the morning sunlight, stale air bringing a faint odor of decay. Looking to my right, I saw a small bathroom with shaving gear laying haphazardly near the sink. Beyond, I could see a bedroom, single-unmade bed, trousers on the floor. Next to the front door was a small kitchen area with a counter that appeared clean. This is where I placed my nursing bag.

"Told that hospital doctor I didn't want anyone checking up on me," shaking his head without looking my direction. "Nobody listens…"

"Just wanted to make sure you were settled at home, won't take much of your time". I reached out my hand toward Joseph; he shook his head with a grimace, turned and sat on an overstuffed brown chair. I noticed the purple spots on his arms, probably from blood draws at the hospital, I thought. Pulling my blood pressure equipment from the bag, I approached him and asked for an arm to "measure his pressure."

With a sigh, he held out his arm and I proceeded to take his pressure, count his radial pulse and record the findings for my records. "Your pressure is a little low this morning. Have you taken morning meds?"

"Hate medications, doctors always are pushing the stuff," he replied. Nodding, I decided against teaching him of the need to take his heart meds. Despite his grumbling, he took the meds when I poured them, without comment. The morning visit

continued with a review of his condition and a promise to return

in a few days.

My visits with Joseph continued for several weeks, with our

relationship gently softening. On one visit, he told me of his

wife's recent death, admitting that her hospice nurse was the only

nurse he trusted. His slow speech and seeming withdrawal from

the outside world signaled need for intervention. With advice of

his physician, I arranged a visit to a mental health facility where

he could be evaluated for depression. Later, the psychiatrist

reported that he gave Joseph samples of medications – only to

see him throw them in the waste-basket on the way out of his

office.

Providing care to an angry patient requires patience to look

beyond their words and gestures to the probable reason for the

outbursts. Joseph was followed by a mental health nurse on my

team who became so upset with his noncompliance and wanted

to discharge him from home care. After our discussions, she agreed that his grief was likely an underlying cause of his depression and outbursts of anger.

Bess Jones was a tall, stately woman with short white hair who was referred for home care after hospital discharge and recovery from a fall. She was evaluated in the hospital emergency room and found to have no fractures. Physical therapists suggested she receive a walker and cane to prevent future falls. She needed help with bathing and dressing – but few aides could tolerate her outbursts of anger. When we learned that she had been a Director of a Nursing Home, we began to listen to her verbal words differently. During a lengthy career, she had been in charge and had difficulty with adjusting to this dependent role. Bess was angry with her loss of independence and projecting it on her aides.

DIVERSITY – APPRECIATION AND RESPECT

Hana, a petite, soft-spoken home health field nurse, stopped

outside my New York office door and bowed. She and her

Japanese husband returned from a two-week trip to their

ancestral home. I knew little about Hana, except that she was

assigned to work Japanese patients, and she was known as an

efficient and caring nurse.

I bowed in return, realizing this form of greeting would

likely be more acceptable than a warm hug. She stood just

outside the threshold with a pensive look on her face.

"Come in", I gestured toward one of the chairs near my

desk. "Sorry to learn of your father's death". The news of his

unexpected passing was relayed to me earlier in the week. There

was a rap on the door and Judith, my secretary, motioned for me

to step outside the office, so I excused myself to learn what the

urgency could be. When I returned, minutes later, I found Hana

standing, pit of direct sight, behind the office door weeping. The image of this beautiful girl hiding her tears leaves me with a lasting respect for Japanese culture. Her home land cultural origins are attributed to for maintaining self-control in distressed times. While I don't remember the details of my response to her sobs, I hope that I allowed her time to grieve.

Moving from Iowa to New York City introduced me to experiences with our country's rich diversity. A Jewish neighbor invited me to Shabbat in her one-room apartment, where I was introduced to ancient traditions of the Jewish religion. My Italian home care nurses told me of their Christmas dinner of octopus, instead of my usual ham or turkey.

Our home health agency received referrals to care for patients from a Russian Community that resided in Queens. Many of the elderly moved to America with children. They could not speak or read English, showing signs of loneliness and depression. When left alone with an aide, they likely felt uncomfortable. One such grand lady was eighty-five-year old Vesna, who moved to America with her daughter Svetlana. Our agency was asked to provide Vesna with personal care and daily activities, while

Svetlana was at work. We developed a contractual with an

agency known for meeting needs of Jewish patients, discovering

aides who could provide the care. They introduced our agency

with a registered nurse who spoke Russian. Her Jewish

background (a Rabbi's wife) was valuable to help this group of

patients.

Months later, Svetlana called and requested an

appointment with me. It took me a minute to remember her.

Svetlana referred to herself as "Lana" and wanted prompting on

how to respond to a job interview. She had been an accountant

in her home country and wanted to apply for an opening in the

Queens hospital. Svetlana referred to herself as "Lana", probably

in a need to adapt to her new community. Applying an

interviewing for employment was unfamiliar territory to her.

SHOOTING AT ASSISTED LIVING FACILITY

"Please come and bring your psych nurses," says the Director. I recognize the high-pitched voice of voice of Judy – who is in charge of the assisted living facility. It is a sunny Saturday morning and I was working on preparations for an accreditation visit of the health care organization. Without understanding the reason for her hurried call, I phone three nurses and ask them to come at Judy's request.

The bright yellow police tape coiled across the main entrance of the building prevents us from entering. I park my car behind other cars that lined the road shoulder. Two police cars are nearby, lights flashing, and a uniformed officer standing near the front entrance. Entering through a side door, I sense the tension in the air. Nurses and aides wear worried faces, while elderly residents appeared to more comfused than usual – wandering around as though uprooted.

Within minutes the chief psychiatrist arrives and gathers the staff and our home health nurses in the hallway to direct activities.

There had been a shooting in the front lobby of the facility. One of the kitchen aides entered though a side door, walked to the seating area in the front lobby and fired a pistol. Two home health aides had abdominal bullet wounds and were rushed to the hospital. The suspect ran outside into the woods near the building.

Dr. Benjamin explains that most of the residents have problems with short-term memory. This could be a blessing because most will have little memory of the incident. We are asked to help calm any agitated residents while the facility staff work on restoring normalcy. He told the group that we would reconvene later in the afternoon to talk about handling our anxiety – as dealing with the emotional trauma was something we would experience.

I walked into the dining room and joined a table of four residents who complained about their late breakfast. "How hard can it be to fry an egg?" said a blue-grey haired lady with thick horn-rimmed glasses. An elderly man looked at me from under a baseball cap with "U.S. Marines" embroidered on the rim to ask for his aide. "She comes every day, was here just twenty minutes ago, and now disappeared." I listened to answer questions and redirected resident concerns until the facility recreational director arrived on scene. Terry cranked up the record player with 40's era music, inviting residents to a "sing-along" session in the large dayroom.

With a sense of calm returned to the environment, I drive to the hospital to see the condition of the aides. Both have abdominal injuries and are treated to manage their wounds and loss of blood. The events of the morning shift my focus to prevention of similar violent acts. Scanning the internet for clues, I find facility policies on workplace violence that include education and need for all staff to report any clues of danger to administration.

Monday morning arrives and the shooting is on everyone's mind. Local news reports carry the story with interviews of facility staff. The Administrator calls a meeting of all staff that were present the previous Saturday. He leads the discussion with a Creole translating his words into the native language of many Haitian immigrant staff. Having words in their native language may help

in understanding. When the conversation began, I noted tears

from kitchen staff and aides. The morning message was to convey

support for anyone who needed counseling with the aftermath.

Today, workplace violence continues to happen and injure far

more people. Hospital and healthcare facilities have entrance

restrictions to require photo identification badges. The assisted

living facility entrance installed a buzzer for entrance. New hire

orientation includes safety measures for security. Many require

background checks as part of the hiring process.

WEATHER WOES

The big red warning swirled toward the Florida Peninsula

on the television screen of my Seattle hotel room. Hurricane

winds gathered speed and swept across land toward our home on

the Atlantic shore. I watched in horror and felt helpless being

more than 1500 miles from home. My trip to the west coast was

to participate in a home care conference. Category 1 Wilma was a storm predicted to hit the west coast of our state; we were not in the path of destruction. A category one storm does little damage – hardly worth the effort to put hurricane shutters over the windows. Today, I was reminded of the unpredictability of mother nature.

Quickly changing my flight plans, I arrived home to find our home without damage except for tree limbs that were strewn over the yard. We had no electricity and used a camping stove to heat canned goods, using candles for light at nightfall. My immediate concerns were for patients that depended on our care. Many had been relocated to shelters, others remained at home without needed sustenance. Plans were developed to prioritize for meeting needs.

Gasoline for cars was a shortage that created a barrier for nurses and aides to reach patient homes. Our Director decided to collect five-gallon gas cans and drive north where there was ample supply. Returning with the gas, each nurse or aide was informed that he/she could come to the office to refill their auto tanks when their gas gauge was less than half full. Three staff members formed a team to make peanut butter sandwiches, from donated supplies, to make food to deliver to hungry patients. One elderly man who lived alone called his aide "my angel" saying, "seeing her walk to my door with food meant the world to me".

One staunch eighty year old woman refused to leave her sixth floor, ocean side condo to evacuate to a shelter. We called her son to plead with her. He told us "she has a mind of her own and refused to intervene. As the rains pelted and winds roared, my thoughts were with her – dreading what we might find in the morning. When roads were safe for travel, nurses drove to find her happily in her apartment, without electricity, but smiling at our chagrin.

During another hurricane, I received a call from an aide, Jessica, who drove through the rains to reach her patient's home. Drenching rains left her wet and shivering. She asked the patient's wife for dry clothes – and felt the shame from the woman's scowl, as she handed her a towel. Anger at this response, I relayed the incident to my husband who offered that this was likely because my aide was black.

The Midwest home health staff dealt with snow, cold weather, and icy roads. Donning snow boots, with snow tires on my car, I continued to see patients for wound care and other necessary services. Torrential summer rains caused flooding for lands close to rivers. One rainstorm brought deluges into the Mississippi river, overflowing the banks and streets. Our home health office in Davenport, Iowa was blocks away from the river, but close enough to the floods. When waters subsided, I drove to the two-story brick building to check the status of our facilities and records. Water had engulfed the basement, where services to private care patients were managed. Looking down the stairway, I first saw desk phones floating. Our agency staff worked from the upper floors until the waters subsided.

On Retirement

Time is my enemy.

Calendar pages fade and fall, my

Life winds down like a worn-out spring.

A relentless alarm wrings a warning,

Reminding that change is near.

Colleagues rush by without a glance, or

Hover near, like flies that swarm on ripe plums.

I am lost in a foreign land searching to

Turn back the clock. Seeking a soul surgeon to

Crush the mounting ache in my gut.

Racing around for help, the search is futile,

My deadline is near, I face an empty void.

Time is my enemy.

*Retirement from Home Health was a difficult transition for me.
I found a need to fill my days with purpose and have found that
volunteering solves that vacancy.*

14683637R10067